ireland

PHOTOGRAPHS BY MICHAEL DIGGIN

Catalog No. D230
Published by Pomegranate Communications, Inc.
Box 808022, Petaluma CA 94975

Available in the UK and mainland Europe from Pomegranate Europe Ltd.
Unit 1, Heathcote Business Centre, Hurlbutt Road, Warwick, Warwickshire CV34 6TD, UK

Pomegranate also publishes the 2009 calendar *Scotland* and more than 150 others in wall, mini wall, engagement, specialty, and 365-day tear-off formats. In addition to calendars, our extensive line of products and publications includes books, posters, postcards, books of postcards, boxed postcard sets, notecards, notecard folios, boxed notecard sets, magnets, mousepads, Knowledge Cards®, birthday books, journals, address books, jigsaw puzzles, designer gift wrap, stationery sets, and bookmarks. For more information or to place an order, please contact Pomegranate Communications, Inc., 800 227 1428, www.pomegranate.com.

Front cover: Thatched house, County Clare

Designed by Ronni Madrid

2009 ENGAGEMENT CALENDAR

Dates in color indicate US federal holidays.
Dates listed for all astronomical events in this calendar are based on Coordinated Universal Time (UTC),
the worldwide system of civil timekeeping. UTC is essentially equivalent to Greenwich Mean Time.
Moon phases and American, Canadian, and UK holidays are noted.

● NEW MOON ☽ FIRST QUARTER ○ FULL MOON ☾ LAST QUARTER

I was born on a storm-swept rock and hate the soft growth of sun-baked lands where there is no frost in men's bones.

—Liam O'Flaherty (1896–1984)

monday

29 364

tuesday

30 365

wednesday

31 366

NEW YEAR'S DAY

thursday

1 1

BANK HOLIDAY (SCOTLAND)

friday

2 2

KILLARNEY, COUNTY KERRY

saturday

3 3

sunday

☽ 4 4

s	m	t	w	t	f	s
				1	2	3
4	5	6	7	8	9	10
11	12	13	14	15	16	17
18	19	20	21	22	23	24
25	26	27	28	29	30	31

JANUARY

January

Oh! Garryowen may be more gay
Than this quiet street of Ballibay;
And I know the sun shines softly
*   down*
On the river that passes my native
*   town.*

But there's not—I say it with joy
*   and pride—*
Better man than mine in Munster
*   wide;*
And Limerick town has no happier
*   hearth*
Than mine has been with my man
*   of the North.*
                    —Thomas D'Arcy McGee
                              (1825–1868)

ADARE, COUNTY LIMERICK

s	m	t	w	t	f	s
				1	2	3
4	5	6	7	8	9	10
11	12	13	14	15	16	17
18	19	20	21	22	23	24
25	26	27	28	29	30	31

JANUARY

monday
5 5

tuesday
6 6

wednesday
7 7

thursday
8 8

friday
9 9

saturday
10 10

sunday
11 11

January

On some island I long to be,
a rocky promontory, looking on
the coiling surface of the sea.

To see the waves, crest on crest
of the great shining ocean,
  composing
a hymn to the creator, without
  rest.

—St. Columcille (521–597)

**COTTAGE ON GALWAY BAY,
COUNTY CLARE**

s	m	t	w	t	f	s
				1	2	3
4	5	6	7	8	9	10
11	12	13	14	15	16	17
18	19	20	21	22	23	24
25	26	27	28	29	30	31

JANUARY

monday
12 12

tuesday
13 13

wednesday
14 14

thursday
15 15

friday
16 16

saturday
17 17

sunday
☾ 18 18

January

In Ireland the inevitable never happens and the unexpected constantly occurs.
—Sir John Pentland Mahaffy
(1839–1919)

monday
19   19

tuesday
20   20

wednesday
21   21

thursday
22   22

friday
23   23

ASKEATON, COUNTY LIMERICK

saturday
24   24

sunday
25   25

s	m	t	w	t	f	s
				1	2	3
4	5	6	7	8	9	10
11	12	13	14	15	16	17
18	19	20	21	22	23	24
25	26	27	28	29	30	31

JANUARY

*Who were the builders? Question
   not the silence
That settles on the lake for ever-
   more,
Save when the sea-bird screams
   and to the islands
The echo answers from the steep-
   cliffed shore.*
   —William Larminie (1849–1900)

**POUL NA BROAN DOLMEN,
COUNTY CLARE**

s	m	t	w	t	f	s
1	2	3	4	5	6	7
8	9	10	11	12	13	14
15	16	17	18	19	20	21
22	23	24	25	26	27	28

FEBRUARY

LUNAR NEW YEAR

monday
● **26** 26

tuesday
27 27

wednesday
28 28

thursday
29 29

friday
30 30

saturday
31 31

sunday
1 32

February

O the sunshine of old Ireland,
*   when it lies*
On her woods and on her waters;
And gleams through her soft skies,
Tenderly as the lovelight in
her daughters'
Gentle eyes.
*   —John Todhunter (1839—1916)*

CLOON LAKE, COUNTY KERRY

s	m	t	w	t	f	s
1	2	3	4	5	6	7
8	9	10	11	12	13	14
15	16	17	18	19	20	21
22	23	24	25	26	27	28

monday
2 33

tuesday
3 34

wednesday
4 35

thursday
5 36

friday
6 37

saturday
7 38

sunday
8 39

february

"You gave me the key of your
heart, my love;
Then why do you make me knock?"
"Oh, that was yesterday, Saints
above!
And last night—I changed the
lock!"
—William B. McBurney
(Carroll Malone) (c. 1855–1892)

monday
◯ **9** ₄₀

tuesday
10 ₄₁

wednesday
11 ₄₂

thursday
12 ₄₃

friday
13 ₄₄

MOONCOIN,
COUNTY KILKENNY

VALENTINE'S DAY
saturday
14 ₄₅

s	m	t	w	t	f	s
1	2	3	4	5	6	7
8	9	10	11	12	13	14
15	16	17	18	19	20	21
22	23	24	25	26	27	28

sunday
15 ₄₆

February

Eternal is the fact that the human creature born in Ireland and brought up in its air is Irish. I have lived for twenty years in Ireland and for seventy-two in England; but the twenty came first, and in Britain I am still a foreigner and shall die one.

—George Bernard Shaw
(1856–1950)

PRESIDENTS' DAY

monday
☾ **16** 47

tuesday
17 48

wednesday
18 49

thursday
19 50

friday
20 51

**CLIFFS OF MOHER,
COUNTY CLARE**

saturday
21 52

sunday
22 53

s	m	t	w	t	f	s
1	2	3	4	5	6	7
8	9	10	11	12	13	14
15	16	17	18	19	20	21
22	23	24	25	26	27	28

FEBRUARY

The grand road from the mountain
goes shining to the sea,
And there is traffic in it and many a
horse and cart,
But the little roads of Cloonagh are
dearer far to me,
And the little roads of Cloonagh go
rambling through my heart.

—Eva Gore-Booth (1870–1926)

GAP OF MAMORE,
COUNTY DONEGAL

s	m	t	w	t	f	s
1	2	3	4	5	6	7
8	9	10	11	12	13	14
15	16	17	18	19	20	21
22	23	24	25	26	27	28
29	30	31				

MARCH

monday
23 54

MARDI GRAS   *tuesday*
24 55

ASH WEDNESDAY   *wednesday*
● 25 56

thursday
26 57

friday
27 58

saturday
28 59

sunday
1 60

Vale of the waterfalls!
Glen of the streams!
Wake from your slumbering!
Wake from your dreams!

Wild sings the mountain-lark,
Bird of the air!
Calling the valley-birds
Up to him there!
      —George Darley (1795–1846)

BLACK VALLEY,
COUNTY KERRY

s	m	t	w	t	f	s
1	2	3	4	5	6	7
8	9	10	11	12	13	14
15	16	17	18	19	20	21
22	23	24	25	26	27	28
29	30	31				

MARCH

monday
2 61

tuesday
3 62

wednesday
☽ **4** 63

thursday
5 64

friday
6 65

saturday
7 66

INTERNATIONAL WOMEN'S DAY
DAYLIGHT SAVING TIME BEGINS
sunday
8 67

march

PURIM (BEGINS AT SUNSET)

monday
9 68

tuesday
10 69

wednesday
○ **11** 70

thursday
12 71

friday
13 72

MAGHEROURTY BAY,
COUNTY DONEGAL

saturday
14 73

sunday
15 74

s	m	t	w	t	f	s
1	2	3	4	5	6	7
8	9	10	11	12	13	14
15	16	17	18	19	20	21
22	23	24	25	26	27	28
29	30	31				

MARCH

When I came back to Dublin I was court-martialled in my absence and sentenced to death in my absence, so I said they could shoot me in my absence.

—Brendan Behan (1923–1964)

monday
16 75

ST. PATRICK'S DAY

tuesday
17 76

wednesday
☾ ## 18 77

thursday
19 78

VERNAL EQUINOX 11:44 UTC

friday
20 79

HA'PENNY BRIDGE, DUBLIN

saturday
21 80

s	m	t	w	t	f	s
1	2	3	4	5	6	7
8	9	10	11	12	13	14
15	16	17	18	19	20	21
22	23	24	25	26	27	28
29	30	31				

MARCH

MOTHERING SUNDAY (UK)

sunday
22 81

Over the dim blue hills
Strays a wild river,
Over the dim blue hills
Rests my heart ever.

Dearer and brighter than
Jewels and pearl,
Dwells she in beauty there,
Maire, my girl.
—John Keegan Casey (1846—1870)

**WICKLOW GAP,
COUNTY WICKLOW**

s	m	t	w	t	f	s
1	2	3	4	5	6	7
8	9	10	11	12	13	14
15	16	17	18	19	20	21
22	23	24	25	26	27	28
29	30	31				

MARCH

monday
23 82

tuesday
24 83

wednesday
25 84

thursday
26 85

friday
27 86

saturday
28 87

SUMMER TIME BEGINS (UK)
sunday
29 88

Not a sound or a motion
Is over the lake,
But the whisper of ripples
As shoreward they break;
My skiff wakes no ruffle
The waters among;
Then listen, dear maid,
To thy true lover's song.

—J. J. Callanan (1795–1828)

monday
30 89

tuesday
31 90

wednesday
1 91

thursday
☽ **2** 92

friday
3 93

ENNISKILLEN REGIMENTAL MUSEUM, COUNTY FERMANAGH

saturday
4 94

s	m	t	w	t	f	s
			1	2	3	4
5	6	7	8	9	10	11
12	13	14	15	16	17	18
19	20	21	22	23	24	25
26	27	28	29	30		

APRIL

PALM SUNDAY

sunday
5 95

And glittering fanes, and lofty
towers
All on this fairy isle are seen:
And waving trees, and shady
bowers,
With more than mortal verdure
green . . .
—Luke Aylmer Connolly (d. 1883)

monday

6 96

tuesday

7 97

PASSOVER (BEGINS AT SUNSET)   *wednesday*

8 98

thursday

○ **9** 99

GOOD FRIDAY   *friday*

10 100

LOUGH SLAT, COUNTY KERRY

saturday

11 101

EASTER   *sunday*

12 102

s	m	t	w	t	f	s
			1	2	3	4
5	6	7	8	9	10	11
12	13	14	15	16	17	18
19	20	21	22	23	24	25
26	27	28	29	30		

APRIL

'Tis a strange thing ... that among us people can't agree the whole week, because they go different ways upon Sundays.
—George Farquhar (1678–1707)

CATHEDRAL OF ST. CANICE, COUNTY KILKENNY

s	m	t	w	t	f	s
			1	2	3	4
5	6	7	8	9	10	11
12	13	14	15	16	17	18
19	20	21	22	23	24	25
26	27	28	29	30		

APRIL

EASTER MONDAY (CANADA, UK)

monday
13 103

tuesday
14 104

wednesday
15 105

thursday
16 106

friday
☾ **17** 107

saturday
18 108

sunday
19 109

April

My one claim to originality among Irishmen is that I have never made a speech.

—George Moore (1852–1933)

DUNAGORE CASTLE, COUNTY CLARE

s	m	t	w	t	f	s
			1	2	3	4
5	6	7	8	9	10	11
12	13	14	15	16	17	18
19	20	21	22	23	24	25
26	27	28	29	30		

APRIL

monday
20 110

tuesday
21 111

EARTH DAY   *wednesday*
22 112

thursday
23 113

friday
24 114

saturday
● **25** 115

sunday
26 116

Oh, 'twas smartly I settled my bea-
　ver hat on me,
The blackthorn stick and the coat
　that flattered me,
And over the ditches I fled like a
　bat from her,
Home to Kerry, like a scalded cat
　from her,
Oh-roh! . . .

Where is he now, oh where is that
　vagabond?
Make haste and be after him,
　carry him back to me,
That cursed rogue, that blathering
　Kerryman,
Breaking my heart with his rakish
　merriment,
Oh-roh! . . .
　　　　—Owen Roe O'Sullivan
　　　　　　(1748–1784)

**COUMEENOLE STRAND,
COUNTY KERRY**

s	m	t	w	t	f	s
					1	2
3	4	5	6	7	8	9
10	11	12	13	14	15	16
17	18	19	20	21	22	23
24	25	26	27	28	29	30
31						

MAY

monday
27 117

tuesday
28 118

wednesday
29 119

thursday
30 120

friday
☽ **1** 121

saturday
2 122

sunday
3 123

MAY

Our Irish blunders are never blunders of the heart.
—Maria Edgeworth
(1767–1849)

BANK HOLIDAY (UK)
monday
4 124

CINCO DE MAYO
tuesday
5 125

wednesday
6 126

thursday
7 127

friday
8 128

LOUGH DERG, COUNTY CLARE

saturday
○ **9** 129

MOTHER'S DAY
sunday
10 130

s	m	t	w	t	f	s
					1	2
3	4	5	6	7	8	9
10	11	12	13	14	15	16
17	18	19	20	21	22	23
24	25	26	27	28	29	30
31						

MAY

How often have I paused on every
 charm,
The sheltered cot, the cultivated
 farm,
The never-failing brook, the busy
 mill,
The decent church that topped the
neighboring hill,
The hawthorn bush, with seats
 beneath
the shade,
For talking age and whispering
 lovers made!
  —Oliver Goldsmith (1728–1774)

CLIFDEN, COUNTY GALWAY

s	m	t	w	t	f	s
					1	2
3	4	5	6	7	8	9
10	11	12	13	14	15	16
17	18	19	20	21	22	23
24	25	26	27	28	29	30
31						

MAY

monday
11 131

tuesday
12 132

wednesday
13 133

thursday
14 134

friday
15 135

ARMED FORCES DAY   *saturday*
16 136

sunday
☾ **17** 137

MAY

*At Glendalough lived a young
    saint,*
On odor of sanctity dwelling,
An old-fashioned odor, which now
We seldom or never are smelling;
A book or a hook were to him
The utmost extent of his wishes;
*Now, a snatch at the "Lives of the
    Saints";*
*Then a catch at the lives of the
    fishes.*
            —Samuel Lover (1797–1868)

**GLENDALOUGH ROUND
TOWER, COUNTY WICKLOW**

monday
18 138

tuesday
19 139

wednesday
20 140

thursday
21 141

friday
22 142

saturday
23 143

sunday
● 24 144

s	m	t	w	t	f	s
					1	2
3	4	5	6	7	8	9
10	11	12	13	14	15	16
17	18	19	20	21	22	23
24	25	26	27	28	29	30
31						

MAY

When I was a maid,
Nor of lovers afraid,
My mother cried, "Girl, never listen
   to men."
Her lectures were long
But I thought her quite wrong,
And I said, "Mother, whom should
   I listen to, then?"
                —James Kenney (1780–1849)

**THATCHED COTTAGE,
COUNTY WEXFORD**

MEMORIAL DAY
BANK HOLIDAY (UK)

monday
25 145

tuesday
26 146

wednesday
27 147

thursday
28 148

friday
29 149

saturday
30 150

sunday
☽ 31 151

s	m	t	w	t	f	s
					1	2
3	4	5	6	7	8	9
10	11	12	13	14	15	16
17	18	19	20	21	22	23
24	25	26	27	28	29	30
31						

MAY

*I pedalled on towards Athlone
through slashing rain across
brown miles of harvested bog—
looking like a child's dream of a
world made of chocolate.*
                    —Dervla Murphy (b. 1931)

monday

1 152

tuesday

2 153

wednesday

3 154

thursday

4 155

friday

5 156

**ATHLONE,
COUNTY WESTMEATH**

saturday

6 157

s	m	t	w	t	f	s
	1	2	3	4	5	6
7	8	9	10	11	12	13
14	15	16	17	18	19	20
21	22	23	24	25	26	27
28	29	30				

sunday

○ **7** 158

Amid the throng she passed along
the meadow-floor;
Spring seemed to smile on Earth
awhile, and then no more.
—James Clarence Mangan
(1803–1849)

CROHY HEAD,
COUNTY DONEGAL

s	m	t	w	t	f	s
	1	2	3	4	5	6
7	8	9	10	11	12	13
14	15	16	17	18	19	20
21	22	23	24	25	26	27
28	29	30				

JUNE

monday
8 159

tuesday
9 160

wednesday
10 161

thursday
11 162

friday
12 163

saturday
13 164

FLAG DAY
sunday
14 165

. . . and then I asked him with my eyes to ask again yes and then he asked me would I yes to say yes my mountain flower and first I put my arms around him yes and drew him down to me so he could feel my breasts all perfume yes and his heart was going like mad and yes I said yes I will Yes.

—James Joyce (1882–1941),
from *Ulysses* (1922)

**POWERSCOURT HOUSE,
COUNTY WICKLOW**

s	m	t	w	t	f	s
	1	2	3	4	5	6
7	8	9	10	11	12	13
14	15	16	17	18	19	20
21	22	23	24	25	26	27
28	29	30				

JUNE

monday
☾ **15** 166

BLOOMSDAY
tuesday
16 167

wednesday
17 168

thursday
18 169

friday
19 170

saturday
20 171

FATHER'S DAY
SUMMER SOLSTICE 05:45 UTC
sunday
21 172

I found in Munster, unfettered of
   any,
Kings and queens, and poets a
many—
Poets well skilled in music and
measure,
Prosperous doings, mirth and
pleasure.
                    —James Clarence Mangan
                         (1803–1849)

RIVER LEE, CORK CITY

s	m	t	w	t	f	s
	1	2	3	4	5	6
7	8	9	10	11	12	13
14	15	16	17	18	19	20
21	22	23	24	25	26	27
28	29	30				

JUNE

monday
22 173

tuesday
23 174

wednesday
24 175

thursday
25 176

friday
26 177

saturday
27 178

sunday
28 179

A soft day, thank God!
A wind from the south
With a honeyed mouth;
A scent of drenching leaves,
Briar and beech and lime,
White elder-flower and thyme
And the soaking grass smells
  sweet,
Crushed by my two bare feet,
While the rain drips,
Drips, drips, drips from the eaves.
  —Winifred M. Letts (1882–1936)

COTTAGE IN ADARE,
COUNTY LIMERICK

s	m	t	w	t	f	s
			1	2	3	4
5	6	7	8	9	10	11
12	13	14	15	16	17	18
19	20	21	22	23	24	25
26	27	28	29	30	31	

JULY

monday
☽ **29** 180

tuesday
30 181

CANADA DAY (CANADA)   *wednesday*
1 182

thursday
2 183

INDEPENDENCE DAY OBSERVED   *friday*
3 184

INDEPENDENCE DAY   *saturday*
4 185

sunday
5 186

july

The only business of the head in the world is to bow a ceaseless obeisance to the heart.
—William Butler Yeats
(1865–1939)

monday
6 ₁₈₇

tuesday
○ 7 ₁₈₈

wednesday
8 ₁₈₉

thursday
9 ₁₉₀

friday
10 ₁₉₁

CLARE ISLAND, COUNTY MAYO

saturday
11 ₁₉₂

s	m	t	w	t	f	s
			1	2	3	4
5	6	7	8	9	10	11
12	13	14	15	16	17	18
19	20	21	22	23	24	25
26	27	28	29	30	31	

sunday
12 ₁₉₃

JULY

An isle of trees full foliaged in a
meadow,
Along whose quiet grassy shores
below
The white sheep bathe in level
lengths of shadow,
And sweet airs amiable as sum-
mer blow
Warmly and faint among the
happy leaves,
Loving each other in a green
repose . . .

—Thomas Caulfield Irwin
(1823–1892)

NORTH OF CONG,
COUNTY MAYO

s	m	t	w	t	f	s
			1	2	3	4
5	6	7	8	9	10	11
12	13	14	15	16	17	18
19	20	21	22	23	24	25
26	27	28	29	30	31	

BANK HOLIDAY (N. IRELAND)

monday
13 194

tuesday
14 195

wednesday
☾ **15** 196

thursday
16 197

friday
17 198

saturday
18 199

sunday
19 200

JULY

Wisdom is the comb given to a man after he has lost his hair.
—J. P. Dunleavy (b. 1926)

KYLEMORE ABBEY,
COUNTY GALWAY

s	m	t	w	t	f	s
			1	2	3	4
5	6	7	8	9	10	11
12	13	14	15	16	17	18
19	20	21	22	23	24	25
26	27	28	29	30	31	

JULY

monday
20 201

tuesday
21 202

wednesday
22 203

thursday
23 204

friday
24 205

saturday
25 206

sunday
26 207

I am a wave of the sea
And the foam of the wave
And the wind of the foam
And the wings of the wind.
—Joseph Mary Plunkett
(1887–1916)

monday
27 208

tuesday
☽ **28** 209

wednesday
29 210

thursday
30 211

friday
31 212

**BALLYDONEGAN BAY,
COUNTY CORK**

saturday
1 213

sunday
2 214

s	m	t	w	t	f	s
						1
2	3	4	5	6	7	8
9	10	11	12	13	14	15
16	17	18	19	20	21	22
23	24	25	26	27	28	29
30	31					

AUGUST

August

What they do in heaven we are ignorant of; what they do not do we are told expressly.
—Jonathan Swift (1667–1745)

BUNRATTY CASTLE, COUNTY CLARE

s	m	t	w	t	f	s
						1
2	3	4	5	6	7	8
9	10	11	12	13	14	15
16	17	18	19	20	21	22
23	24	25	26	27	28	29
30	31					

AUGUST

CIVIC HOLIDAY (CANADA, MOST PROVINCES)
BANK HOLIDAY (SCOTLAND)

monday
3 215

tuesday
4 216

wednesday
5 217

thursday
○ 6 218

friday
7 219

saturday
8 220

sunday
9 221

An Irish novelist gets from the Irish people a certain reverence, a good measure of kindliness, considerable latitude in conduct and thought: in fine he gets his due from a God-fearing people. But he must not forget that his first duty is homeward.

—Donn Byrne (1889–1929)

monday
10 222

tuesday
11 223

wednesday
12 224

thursday
☾ ## 13 225

friday
14 226

**WEXFORD HARBOUR,
COUNTY WEXFORD**

saturday
15 227

sunday
16 228

s	m	t	w	t	f	s
						1
2	3	4	5	6	7	8
9	10	11	12	13	14	15
16	17	18	19	20	21	22
23	24	25	26	27	28	29
30	31					

AUGUST

august

So simple is the earth we tread,
So quick with love and life her
  frame,
Ten thousand years have dawned
  and fled,
And still her magic is the same.
  —Stopford A. Brooke (1832–1916)

**IVERAGH PENINSULA,
COUNTY KERRY**

s	m	t	w	t	f	s
						1
2	3	4	5	6	7	8
9	10	11	12	13	14	15
16	17	18	19	20	21	22
23	24	25	26	27	28	29
30	31					

AUGUST

monday
17 229

tuesday
18 230

wednesday
19 231

thursday
20 232

friday
21 233

saturday
22 234

sunday
23 235

August

*There is not in the wide world
a valley so sweet
As that vale in whose bosom the
bright waters meet;
O the last rays of feeling and life
must depart,
Ere the bloom of that valley shall
fade from my heart.*

       —Thomas Moore (1779–1852)

**DINGLE PENINSULA,
COUNTY KERRY**

s	m	t	w	t	f	s
						1
2	3	4	5	6	7	8
9	10	11	12	13	14	15
16	17	18	19	20	21	22
23	24	25	26	27	28	29
30	31					

AUGUST

monday
24 236

tuesday
25 237

wednesday
26 238

thursday
☽ **27** 239

friday
28 240

saturday
29 241

sunday
30 242

Dá gcaillfí an Ghaeilge chaillfí Éire.
[If the Irish language were to be lost, Ireland would perish.]
—Patrick Pearse (1879–1916)

ROADSIDE PUB, COUNTY TIPPERARY

s	m	t	w	t	f	s
		1	2	3	4	5
6	7	8	9	10	11	12
13	14	15	16	17	18	19
20	21	22	23	24	25	26
27	28	29	30			

SEPTEMBER

BANK HOLIDAY (UK EXCEPT SCOTLAND)

monday
31 243

tuesday
1 244

wednesday
2 245

thursday
3 246

friday
○ 4 247

saturday
5 248

sunday
6 249

september

LABOR DAY (US, CANADA)

monday
7 250

tuesday
8 251

wednesday
9 252

thursday
10 253

friday
11 254

**ROCK OF CASHEL,
COUNTY TIPPERARY**

saturday
☾ 12 255

sunday
13 256

s	m	t	w	t	f	s
		1	2	3	4	5
6	7	8	9	10	11	12
13	14	15	16	17	18	19
20	21	22	23	24	25	26
27	28	29	30			

SEPTEMBER

september

I used to walk the morning stream,
The meadows fresh with the dew's
   wet gleam,
Beside the woods, in the hillside's
   shade,
No shadow or doubt on the light-
   some day.
It'd gladden the heart in a broken
   man,
Spent without profit, vigour or
   plan.
   —Brian Merriman (1747–1805)

**CARAGH RIVER,
COUNTY KERRY**

monday
14 ₂₅₇

tuesday
15 ₂₅₈

wednesday
16 ₂₅₉

thursday
17 ₂₆₀

ROSH HASHANAH (BEGINS AT SUNSET)

friday
18 ₂₆₁

saturday
19 ₂₆₂

sunday
20 ₂₆₃

s	m	t	w	t	f	s
		1	2	3	4	5
6	7	8	9	10	11	12
13	14	15	16	17	18	19
20	21	22	23	24	25	26
27	28	29	30			

SEPTEMBER

september

The safest road to hell is the gradual one—the gentle slope, soft underfoot, without sudden turn-ings, without milestones, without signposts.

—C. S. Lewis (1898–1963)

INTERNATIONAL DAY OF PEACE

monday

21 264

AUTUMNAL EQUINOX 21:18 UTC

tuesday

22 265

wednesday

23 266

thursday

24 267

friday

25 268

**DUNAGORE CASTLE,
COUNTY CLARE**

saturday

☽ ## 26 269

s	m	t	w	t	f	s
		1	2	3	4	5
6	7	8	9	10	11	12
13	14	15	16	17	18	19
20	21	22	23	24	25	26
27	28	29	30			

SEPTEMBER

YOM KIPPUR (BEGINS AT SUNSET)

sunday

27 270

O bear me my blessing afar to
*   the West,*
For the heart in my bosom is
*   broken; I fail.*
Should death of a sudden now
*   pierce my breast*
I should die of the love that I bear
*   the Gael!*
*   —St. Columcille (521–597)*

FANAD HEAD,
COUNTY DONEGAL

s	m	t	w	t	f	s
				1	2	3
4	5	6	7	8	9	10
11	12	13	14	15	16	17
18	19	20	21	22	23	24
25	26	27	28	29	30	31

OCTOBER

monday
28 271

tuesday
29 272

wednesday
30 273

thursday
1 274

friday
2 275

saturday
3 276

sunday
○ **4** 277

october

A little sun, a little rain,
A soft wind blowing from the west,
And woods and fields are sweet
  again.
And warmth within the mountain's
  breast . . .
  —Stopford A. Brooke (1832—1916)

CONNEMARA DISTRICT,
COUNTY GALWAY

s	m	t	w	t	f	s
				1	2	3
4	5	6	7	8	9	10
11	12	13	14	15	16	17
18	19	20	21	22	23	24
25	26	27	28	29	30	31

OCTOBER

monday
5   278

tuesday
6   279

wednesday
7   280

thursday
8   281

friday
9   282

saturday
10   283

sunday
☾ 11   284

october

The hedges are all drowned in
   green grass seas,
And bobbing poppies flare like
   Elmo's light,
While siren-like the pollen-stained
   bees
Drone in the clover depths. And up
   the height
The cuckoo's voice is hoarse and
   broke with joy.
   —Francis Ledwidge (1887–1917)

**LOUGH LEANE CANAL BOATS,
COUNTY KERRY**

s	m	t	w	t	f	s
				1	2	3
4	5	6	7	8	9	10
11	12	13	14	15	16	17
18	19	20	21	22	23	24
25	26	27	28	29	30	31

OCTOBER

COLUMBUS DAY
THANKSGIVING DAY (CANADA)

monday
12 285

tuesday
13 286

wednesday
14 287

thursday
15 288

friday
16 289

saturday
17 290

sunday
18 291

Ah! What woes are mine to bear,
Life's fair morn with clouds
  o'ercasting!
Doomed the victim of despair!
Youth's gay bloom, pale sorrow
  blasting!

Sad the bird that sings alone,
Flies to wilds, unseen to languish,
Pours, unheard, the ceaseless
  moan,
And wastes on desert air its
  anguish!
  —Edmond O'Ryan (c. 1680–1724)

**SCATTERY ISLAND,
COUNTY CLARE**

s	m	t	w	t	f	s
				1	2	3
4	5	6	7	8	9	10
11	12	13	14	15	16	17
18	19	20	21	22	23	24
25	26	27	28	29	30	31

OCTOBER

monday
19 292

tuesday
20 293

wednesday
21 294

thursday
22 295

friday
23 296

UNITED NATIONS DAY
saturday
24 297

SUMMER TIME ENDS (UK)
sunday
25 298

Now Autumn's fire burns slowly
  along the woods,
And day by day the dead leaves fall
  and melt,
And night by night the monitory
  blast
Wails in the key-hold, telling how
  it pass'd
O'er empty fields, or upland
  solitudes,
Or grim wide wave; and now the
  power is felt
Of melancholy, tenderer in its
  moods
Than any joy indulgent summer
  dealt.
—William Allingham (1824–1889)

**LOUGH DERRYCLARE,
COUNTY GALWAY**

monday
☽ **26** 299

tuesday
27 300

wednesday
28 301

thursday
29 302

friday
30 303

HALLOWEEN

saturday
31 304

DAYLIGHT SAVING TIME ENDS

sunday
1 305

s	m	t	w	t	f	s
1	2	3	4	5	6	7
8	9	10	11	12	13	14
15	16	17	18	19	20	21
22	23	24	25	26	27	28
29	30					

NOVEMBER

november

Were I west in green Arran,
Or south in Glanmore,
Where the long ships come laden
With claret in store;
Yet I'd rather than shiploads
Of claret, and ships,
Have your white cup, O'Hara,
Up full at my lips.

   —Turlough Carolan (1670–1738)

**O'BRIEN CASTLE, INISHEER
(ARAN ISLANDS),
COUNTY GALWAY**

s	m	t	w	t	f	s
1	2	3	4	5	6	7
8	9	10	11	12	13	14
15	16	17	18	19	20	21
22	23	24	25	26	27	28
29	30					

NOVEMBER

monday
2 306

tuesday
3 307

wednesday
4 308

thursday
5 309

friday
6 310

saturday
7 311

sunday
8 312

november

*O blame not the bard if he flies to
the bowers
Where pleasure lies carelessly
    smiling
at fame;
He was born for much more, and in
happier hours
His soul might have burned with
a holier flame.*
        —Thomas Moore (1779–1852)

**THATCHED ROOF,
COUNTY WATERFORD**

monday

☾ **9** 313

tuesday

10 314

VETERANS DAY
REMEMBRANCE DAY (CANADA)

wednesday

11 315

thursday

12 316

friday

13 317

saturday

14 318

sunday

15 319

s	m	t	w	t	f	s
1	2	3	4	5	6	7
8	9	10	11	12	13	14
15	16	17	18	19	20	21
22	23	24	25	26	27	28
29	30					

NOVEMBER

november

I met the Love-Talker one eve in the glen,
He was handsomer than any of our handsome young men,
His eyes were blacker than the sloe,
his voice sweeter far
Than the crooning of old Kevin's pipes
beyond in Coolnagar.
                    —Ethna Carbery
          (Anna MacManus; 1866–1902)

COTTAGE ON GALWAY BAY, COUNTY CLARE

s	m	t	w	t	f	s
1	2	3	4	5	6	7
8	9	10	11	12	13	14
15	16	17	18	19	20	21
22	23	24	25	26	27	28
29	30					

NOVEMBER

monday
16 320

tuesday
17 321

wednesday
18 322

thursday
19 323

friday
20 324

saturday
21 325

sunday
22 326

november

> *Freedom is a thing that you cannot cut in two—you are either all free or you are not free.*
> —Eamon De Valera (1882–1975)

monday
23 327

tuesday
☽ **24** 328

wednesday
25 329

THANKSGIVING DAY
thursday
26 330

friday
27 331

CLASSIE BAWN CASTLE, MULLAGHMORE, COUNTY SLIGO

saturday
28 332

sunday
29 333

s	m	t	w	t	f	s
1	2	3	4	5	6	7
8	9	10	11	12	13	14
15	16	17	18	19	20	21
22	23	24	25	26	27	28
29	30					

NOVEMBER

We make out of the quarrel with others, rhetoric, but of the quarrel with ourselves, poetry.

—William Butler Yeats

(1865–1939)

monday

30 334

tuesday

1 335

wednesday

2 336

thursday

3 337

friday

4 338

JOHNSTOWN CASTLE, COUNTY WEXFORD

saturday

5 339

sunday

6 340

s	m	t	w	t	f	s
		1	2	3	4	5
6	7	8	9	10	11	12
13	14	15	16	17	18	19
20	21	22	23	24	25	26
27	28	29	30	31		

DECEMBER

december

Get the advice of everybody whose opinion is worth having—they are very few—and then do what you think best yourself.

—Charles Stewart Parnell
(1846–1891)

**DUNGUAIRE CASTLE,
COUNTY GALWAY**

monday
7 341

tuesday
8 342

wednesday
☽ **9** 343

thursday
10 344

HANUKKAH (BEGINS AT SUNSET)

friday
11 345

saturday
12 346

sunday
13 347

s	m	t	w	t	f	s
		1	2	3	4	5
6	7	8	9	10	11	12
13	14	15	16	17	18	19
20	21	22	23	24	25	26
27	28	29	30	31		

DECEMBER

december

*One wonders in this place, why
anyone is left in Dublin, or London,
or Paris when it would be better
one would think, to live in a tent,
or a hut, with this magnificent
sea and sky, and to breathe this
wonderful air, which is like wine in
one's teeth.*

—John Millington Synge
(1871–1909)

KINGSTON, COUNTY GALWAY

s	m	t	w	t	f	s
		1	2	3	4	5
6	7	8	9	10	11	12
13	14	15	16	17	18	19
20	21	22	23	24	25	26
27	28	29	30	31		

DECEMBER

monday
14 348

tuesday
15 349

wednesday
16 350

thursday
17 351

friday
18 352

saturday
19 353

sunday
20 354

WINTER SOLSTICE 17:47 UTC

Irishness is not primarily a question of birth or blood or language; it is the condition of being involved in the Irish situation, and usually of being mauled by it.

—Conor Cruise O'Brien (b. 1917)

monday
21 355

tuesday
22 356

wednesday
23 357

thursday
☽ 24 358

CHRISTMAS

friday
25 359

CARRICKKILDAVNET CASTLE, COUNTY MAYO

KWANZAA BEGINS
BOXING DAY (CANADA, UK)

saturday
26 360

sunday
27 361

s	m	t	w	t	f	s
		1	2	3	4	5
6	7	8	9	10	11	12
13	14	15	16	17	18	19
20	21	22	23	24	25	26
27	28	29	30	31		

DECEMBER

DEC ✦ JAN

May you live all the days of your life.

—Jonathan Swift (1667–1745)

BOXING DAY OBSERVED (CANADA, UK)

monday
28 ₃₆₂

tuesday
29 ₃₆₃

wednesday
30 ₃₆₄

thursday
◯ 31 ₃₆₅

NEW YEAR'S DAY

friday
1 ₁

**ACHILL ISLAND,
COUNTY MAYO**

saturday
2 ₂

sunday
3 ₃

s	m	t	w	t	f	s
					1	2
3	4	5	6	7	8	9
10	11	12	13	14	15	16
17	18	19	20	21	22	23
24	25	26	27	28	29	30
31						

JANUARY

2009 International Holidays

Following are the dates of major holidays in 2009 for selected countries. Islamic observances are subject to adjustment. Holidays of the United States, United Kingdom, and Canada, and major Jewish holidays, appear on this calendar's grid pages. Pomegranate is not responsible for errors or omissions in this list. Users of this information should confirm dates with local sources before making international travel or business plans.

Please note: Most international holidays that fall on a weekend are observed on the following Monday (or the next working day).

ARGENTINA
1 Jan	New Year's Day
24 Mar	National Day of Memory for Truth and Justice
2 Apr	Veterans Day (Malvinas War Memorial)
9 Apr	Holy Thursday
10 Apr	Good Friday
12 Apr	Easter
1 May	Labor Day
25 May	Revolution Day
20 Jun	Flag Day*
9 Jul	Independence Day
17 Aug	San Martín Day*
12 Oct	Día de la Raza
8 Dec	Immaculate Conception
25 Dec	Christmas

* Observed on the third Monday of the month.

AUSTRALIA
1 Jan	New Year's Day
26 Jan	Australia Day
2 Mar	Labor Day (WA)
9 Mar	Labor Day (Vic)
	Eight Hours Day (Tas)
	Adelaide Cup (SA)
16 Mar	Canberra Day (ACT)
10–13 Apr	Easter Holiday
14 Apr	Easter Tuesday (Tas)
25 Apr	ANZAC Day
4 May	Labor Day (Qld)
	May Day (NT)
1 Jun	Foundation Day (WA)
8 Jun	Queen's Birthday (except WA)
	Volunteer's Day (SA)
3 Aug	Picnic Day (NT)
	Bank Holiday (NSW, ACT)
28 Sep	Queen's Birthday (WA)
5 Oct	Labor Day (NSW, ACT, SA)
3 Nov	Melbourne Cup (ACT)
25 Dec	Christmas
26 Dec	Boxing Day
28 Dec	Proclamation Day (SA)*

* Observed on the first weekday following the Christmas public holiday.

BRAZIL
1 Jan	New Year's Day
20 Jan	São Sebastião Day (Rio de Janeiro)
25 Jan	São Paulo Anniversary (São Paulo)
23–24 Feb	Carnival
25 Feb	Ash Wednesday (morning only)
10 Apr	Good Friday
12 Apr	Easter
21 Apr	Tiradentes Day
1 May	Labor Day
11 Jun	Corpus Christi
7 Sep	Independence Day
12 Oct	Our Lady of Aparecida

2 Nov	All Souls' Day
15 Nov	Proclamation of the Republic
20 Nov	Zumbi dos Palmares Day (Rio de Janeiro, São Paulo)
25 Dec	Christmas
31 Dec	New Year's Eve Bank Holiday

CHINA (SEE ALSO HONG KONG)
1 Jan	New Year's Day
26 Jan	Chinese New Year Holiday begins
1 Feb	Last day of New Year Holiday
1–7 May	Labor Day Holiday
1–7 Oct	National Day Holiday

FRANCE
1 Jan	New Year's Day
12 Apr	Easter
13 Apr	Easter Monday
1 May	Labor Day
8 May	Victory Day (WWII)
21 May	Ascension Day
31 May	Pentecost
1 Jun	Whitmonday
14 Jul	Bastille Day
15 Aug	Assumption Day
1 Nov	All Saints' Day
11 Nov	Armistice Day (WWI)
25 Dec	Christmas

GERMANY
1 Jan	New Year's Day
10 Apr	Good Friday
12 Apr	Easter
13 Apr	Easter Monday
1 May	Labor Day
21 May	Ascension Day
31 May	Pentecost
1 Jun	Whitmonday
3 Oct	Unity Day
25 Dec	Christmas
26 Dec	St. Stephen's Day

HONG KONG
1 Jan	New Year's Day
26–28 Jan	Spring Festival / Lunar New Year
5 Apr	Grave Sweeping Festival
10–13 Apr	Easter Holiday
1 May	Labor Day
2 May	Buddha's Birthday
28 May	Dragon Boat Festival
1 Jul	Special Administrative Region Establishment Day
1 Oct	National Day
5 Oct	Mid-Autumn Festival
26 Oct	Chung Yeung Festival
25 Dec	Christmas
26 Dec	Boxing Day

INDIA
1 Jan	New Year's Day
14 Jan	Makar Sankranti

26 Jan	Republic Day
9 Mar	Prophet Muhammad's Birthday
11 Mar	Holi
3 Apr	Rama Navami
7 Apr	Mahavir Jayanthi
10 Apr	Good Friday
12 Apr	Easter
9 May	Buddha Purnima
15 Aug	Independence Day
20 Sep	Ramzan Id (Eid-al-Fitr)
26–28 Sep	Dussehra
2 Oct	Mahatma Gandhi's Birthday
17 Oct	Diwali (Deepavali)
2 Nov	Guru Nanak's Birthday
27–29 Nov	Bakr-Id (Eid-al-Adha)
18 Dec	Muharram (Islamic New Year)
25 Dec	Christmas

IRELAND
1 Jan	New Year's Day
17 Mar	St. Patrick's Day
10 Apr	Good Friday
12 Apr	Easter
13 Apr	Easter Monday
4 May	May Holiday
1 Jun	June Holiday
3 Aug	August Holiday
26 Oct	October Holiday
25 Dec	Christmas
26 Dec	St. Stephen's Day

ISRAEL
10 Mar	Purim
9 Apr	First day of Pesach
15 Apr	Last day of Pesach
21 Apr	Holocaust Memorial Day
28 Apr	National Memorial Day
29 Apr	Independence Day
29 May	Shavuot
30 Jul	Tisha B'Av
19–20 Sep	Rosh Hashanah
28 Sep	Yom Kippur
3 Oct	First day of Sukkot
10 Oct	Shemini Atzeret/Simhat Torah

ITALY
1 Jan	New Year's Day
6 Jan	Epiphany
12 Apr	Easter
13 Apr	Easter Monday
25 Apr	Liberation Day
1 May	Labor Day
2 Jun	Republic Day
29 Jun	Sts. Peter and Paul (Rome)
15 Aug	Assumption Day
1 Nov	All Saints' Day
8 Dec	Immaculate Conception
25 Dec	Christmas
26 Dec	St. Stephen's Day

JAPAN

1	Jan	New Year's Day
12	Jan	Coming of Age Day
11	Feb	National Foundation Day
20	Mar	Vernal Equinox Holiday
29	Apr	Showa Day
3	May	Constitution Memorial Day
4	May	Greenery Day
5	May	Children's Day
20	Jul	Marine Day
21	Sep	Respect for the Aged Day
22–23	Sep	Autumnal Equinox Holiday
12	Oct	Health and Sports Day
3	Nov	Culture Day
23	Nov	Labor Thanksgiving Day
23	Dec	Emperor's Birthday

MEXICO

1	Jan	New Year's Day
5	Feb	Constitution Day*
21	Mar	Benito Juárez Day†
9	Apr	Holy Thursday
10	Apr	Good Friday
11	Apr	Holy Saturday
12	Apr	Easter
1	May	Labor Day
5	May	Battle of Puebla (Cinco de Mayo)
16	Sep	Independence Day
1	Nov	All Saints Day
2	Nov	All Souls Day (Day of the Dead)
20	Nov	Revolution Day†
12	Dec	Our Lady of Guadalupe
25	Dec	Christmas

* Observed on the first Monday of the month.
† Observed on the third Monday of the month.

NETHERLANDS

1	Jan	New Year's Day
10	Apr	Good Friday
12	Apr	Easter
13	Apr	Easter Monday
30	Apr	Queen's Birthday
4	May	Remembrance Day
5	May	Liberation Day
21	May	Ascension Day
31	May	Pentecost
1	Jun	Whitmonday
25–26	Dec	Christmas Holiday

NEW ZEALAND

1–2	Jan	New Year's Holiday
22	Jan	Provincial Anniversary (Wellington)*
29	Jan	Provincial Anniversary (Auckland)*
6	Feb	Waitangi Day
10	Apr	Good Friday
12	Apr	Easter
13	Apr	Easter Monday
25	Apr	ANZAC Day
1	Jun	Queen's Birthday
26	Oct	Labor Day
13	Nov	Provincial Anniversary (Canterbury)*
25	Dec	Christmas
26	Dec	Boxing Day

* Observed on the closest Monday.

PUERTO RICO

6	Jan	Three Kings Day (Epiphany)
11	Jan	Eugenio María de Hostos Day*
22	Mar	Emancipation Day
10	Apr	Good Friday
12	Apr	Easter
16	Apr	José de Diego Day†
17	Jul	Luis Muñoz Rivera Day†
25	Jul	Constitution Day
27	Jul	José Celso Barbosa Day
12	Oct	Día de la Raza
19	Nov	Discovery of Puerto Rico
24	Dec	Christmas Eve

All US federal holidays also observed.
* Observed on the second Monday of the month.
† Observed on the third Monday of the month.

RUSSIA

1–6	Jan	New Year's Holiday
7	Jan	Orthodox Christmas
23	Feb	Defender of the Motherland Day
9	Mar	International Women's Day
19	Apr	Orthodox Easter
1	May	Spring and Labor Day
11	May	Victory Day
12	Jun	Independence Day
4	Nov	National Unity Day

SINGAPORE

1	Jan	New Year's Day
26–27	Jan	Chinese New Year Holiday
10	Apr	Good Friday
12	Apr	Easter
1	May	Labor Day
9	May	Vesak Day (Buddha's Birthday)
9	Aug	National Day
22	Aug	Beginning of Ramadan
20	Sep	Hari Raya Puasa (Eid-al-Fitr)
17	Oct	Deepavali
27	Nov	Hari Raya Haji (Eid-al-Adha)
25	Dec	Christmas

SOUTH AFRICA

1	Jan	New Year's Day
21	Mar	Human Rights Day
10	Apr	Good Friday
12	Apr	Easter
13	Apr	Family Day
27	Apr	Freedom Day
1	May	Worker's Day
16	Jun	Youth Day
9	Aug	National Women's Day
24	Sep	Heritage Day
16	Dec	Day of Reconciliation
25	Dec	Christmas
26	Dec	Day of Goodwill

SOUTH KOREA

1	Jan	New Year's Day
25–27	Jan	Lunar New Year Holiday
1	Mar	Independence Movement Day
2	May	Birth of Buddha
5	May	Children's Day
6	Jun	Memorial Day
15	Aug	Independence Day
2–4	Oct	Harvest Moon Festival
3	Oct	National Foundation Day
25	Dec	Christmas

SPAIN

1	Jan	New Year's Day
6	Jan	Epiphany
9	Apr	Holy Thursday (Madrid)
10	Apr	Good Friday
12	Apr	Easter
1	May	Labor Day
15	Aug	Assumption Day
12	Oct	National Day
1	Nov	All Saints' Day
6	Dec	Constitution Day
8	Dec	Immaculate Conception
25	Dec	Christmas

SWEDEN

1	Jan	New Year's Day
5	Jan	Epiphany Eve
6	Jan	Epiphany
9	Apr	Maundy Thursday
10	Apr	Good Friday
12	Apr	Easter
13	Apr	Easter Monday
30	Apr	Walpurgis Eve / King's Birthday
1	May	May Day
20	May	Day Before Ascension
21	May	Ascension Day
31	May	Pentecost
6	Jun	National Day
19	Jun	Midsummer Eve
20	Jun	Midsummer Day
30	Oct	All Saints' Eve
31	Oct	All Saints' Day
24	Dec	Christmas Eve
25	Dec	Christmas
26	Dec	Boxing Day
31	Dec	New Year's Eve

SWITZERLAND

1	Jan	New Year's Day
10	Apr	Good Friday
12	Apr	Easter
13	Apr	Easter Monday
21	May	Ascension Day
31	May	Pentecost
1	Jun	Whitmonday
1	Aug	National Day
25	Dec	Christmas

THAILAND

1	Jan	New Year's Day
9	Feb	Makha Bucha Day
6	Apr	Chakri Day
13–15	Apr	Songkran (Thai New Year)
1	May	Labor Day
5	May	Coronation Day
8	May	Visakha Bucha Day (Buddha's Birthday)
7	Jul	Asanha Bucha Day
8	Jul	Khao Phansa (Buddhist Lent begins)
12	Aug	Queen's Birthday
23	Oct	Chulalongkorn Day
2	Nov	Loy Kratong
5	Dec	King's Birthday
10	Dec	Constitution Day
31	Dec	New Year's Eve

2009

JANUARY

s	m	t	w	t	f	s
				1	2	3
4	5	6	7	8	9	10
11	12	13	14	15	16	17
18	19	20	21	22	23	24
25	26	27	28	29	30	31

FEBRUARY

s	m	t	w	t	f	s
1	2	3	4	5	6	7
8	9	10	11	12	13	14
15	16	17	18	19	20	21
22	23	24	25	26	27	28

MARCH

s	m	t	w	t	f	s
1	2	3	4	5	6	7
8	9	10	11	12	13	14
15	16	17	18	19	20	21
22	23	24	25	26	27	28
29	30	31				

APRIL

s	m	t	w	t	f	s
			1	2	3	4
5	6	7	8	9	10	11
12	13	14	15	16	17	18
19	20	21	22	23	24	25
26	27	28	29	30		

MAY

s	m	t	w	t	f	s
					1	2
3	4	5	6	7	8	9
10	11	12	13	14	15	16
17	18	19	20	21	22	23
24	25	26	27	28	29	30
31						

JUNE

s	m	t	w	t	f	s
	1	2	3	4	5	6
7	8	9	10	11	12	13
14	15	16	17	18	19	20
21	22	23	24	25	26	27
28	29	30				

JULY

s	m	t	w	t	f	s
			1	2	3	4
5	6	7	8	9	10	11
12	13	14	15	16	17	18
19	20	21	22	23	24	25
26	27	28	29	30	31	

AUGUST

s	m	t	w	t	f	s
						1
2	3	4	5	6	7	8
9	10	11	12	13	14	15
16	17	18	19	20	21	22
23	24	25	26	27	28	29
30	31					

SEPTEMBER

s	m	t	w	t	f	s
		1	2	3	4	5
6	7	8	9	10	11	12
13	14	15	16	17	18	19
20	21	22	23	24	25	26
27	28	29	30			

OCTOBER

s	m	t	w	t	f	s
				1	2	3
4	5	6	7	8	9	10
11	12	13	14	15	16	17
18	19	20	21	22	23	24
25	26	27	28	29	30	31

NOVEMBER

s	m	t	w	t	f	s
1	2	3	4	5	6	7
8	9	10	11	12	13	14
15	16	17	18	19	20	21
22	23	24	25	26	27	28
29	30					

DECEMBER

s	m	t	w	t	f	s
		1	2	3	4	5
6	7	8	9	10	11	12
13	14	15	16	17	18	19
20	21	22	23	24	25	26
27	28	29	30	31		

JANUARY

s	m	t	w	t	f	s
					1	2
3	4	5	6	7	8	9
10	11	12	13	14	15	16
17	18	19	20	21	22	23
24	25	26	27	28	29	30
31						

FEBRUARY

s	m	t	w	t	f	s
	1	2	3	4	5	6
7	8	9	10	11	12	13
14	15	16	17	18	19	20
21	22	23	24	25	26	27
28						

MARCH

s	m	t	w	t	f	s
	1	2	3	4	5	6
7	8	9	10	11	12	13
14	15	16	17	18	19	20
21	22	23	24	25	26	27
28	29	30	31			

APRIL

s	m	t	w	t	f	s
				1	2	3
4	5	6	7	8	9	10
11	12	13	14	15	16	17
18	19	20	21	22	23	24
25	26	27	28	29	30	

MAY

s	m	t	w	t	f	s
						1
2	3	4	5	6	7	8
9	10	11	12	13	14	15
16	17	18	19	20	21	22
23	24	25	26	27	28	29
30	31					

JUNE

s	m	t	w	t	f	s
		1	2	3	4	5
6	7	8	9	10	11	12
13	14	15	16	17	18	19
20	21	22	23	24	25	26
27	28	29	30			

JULY

s	m	t	w	t	f	s
				1	2	3
4	5	6	7	8	9	10
11	12	13	14	15	16	17
18	19	20	21	22	23	24
25	26	27	28	29	30	31

AUGUST

s	m	t	w	t	f	s
1	2	3	4	5	6	7
8	9	10	11	12	13	14
15	16	17	18	19	20	21
22	23	24	25	26	27	28
29	30	31				

SEPTEMBER

s	m	t	w	t	f	s
			1	2	3	4
5	6	7	8	9	10	11
12	13	14	15	16	17	18
19	20	21	22	23	24	25
26	27	28	29	30		

OCTOBER

s	m	t	w	t	f	s
					1	2
3	4	5	6	7	8	9
10	11	12	13	14	15	16
17	18	19	20	21	22	23
24	25	26	27	28	29	30
31						

NOVEMBER

s	m	t	w	t	f	s
	1	2	3	4	5	6
7	8	9	10	11	12	13
14	15	16	17	18	19	20
21	22	23	24	25	26	27
28	29	30				

DECEMBER

s	m	t	w	t	f	s
			1	2	3	4
5	6	7	8	9	10	11
12	13	14	15	16	17	18
19	20	21	22	23	24	25
26	27	28	29	30	31	

Notes